Violin Grade 7

Pieces

for Trinity Guildhall examinations

2010-2015

Published by:
Trinity College London
89 Albert Embankment
London SE1 7TP UK

T +44 (0)20 7820 6100
F +44 (0)20 7820 6161
E music@trinityguildhall.co.uk
www.trinityguildhall.co.uk

Music processed by New Notations London and Moira Roach.
Printed in England by Halstan & Co. Ltd, Amersham, Bucks.

Andante & Vivace

1st and 2nd movements from Sonata in A, TWV41: A4

Georg Philipp Telemann
(1681-1767)

Andante [♩ = 63–72]

Slurring is editorial. Dynamics have been left to the performer's discretion.

3

Allegro

2nd movement from Sonata in G, K. 301

Wolfgang Amadeus Mozart
(1756-1791)

Editorial dynamics are bracketed. Slurring is editorial.

14

15

Polish Dance

Edmund Severn
(1862-1942)

Allegro con spirito [♩ = 116–138]

(1) At the heel of the bow   (2) Left-hand pizzicato

sempre con fuoco

sempre con fuoco

pizz.

21

⊕ **Coda**

Tempo I

165

poco a poco stringendo

171

con molto fuoco

con molto fuoco

pressez

176

più presto

181

Allegro ritmico

revised version 1999

Anthony Hedges
(born 1931)

Cavatina

Joachim Raff
(1822-1882)

31

stringendo   a tempo primo

Mélodie Arabe
op. 4 no. 5

arr. Samuel Dushkin

Alexander Glazunov
(1865–1936)

(*1*) The small (lower) notes may be omitted in the examination.

Improvisation

István Szelényi
(1904-1972)

Rêverie

Angela Morley
(1924-2009)

Bracketed dynamics are editorial.

42

All pieces in this volume have been edited with regard to current concepts of performance practice. Bowing, fingering, dynamics and articulation have been suggested to assist candidates and their teachers in developing their own interpretations.

Recommended metronome markings are given as a useful, but not definitive, performance guide for all pieces. Those without square brackets are the composer's own indication of the appropriate speed for the music.

Repeats of more than three bars should be omitted unless instructed otherwise in the syllabus or Trinity music book, but all da capo and dal segno instructions should be observed.

Every effort has been made to trace and acknowledge the copyright owners. If any right has been omitted or if any detail is incorrect, Trinity College London apologises and will rectify this in any subsequent reprints following notification.

Trinity College London would like to thank Naomi Yandell, Adrian Eales and Janice Gillard for their editorial work on this book and Robin Hagues and Nigel Yandell for new arrangements/realisations.